Piano Exam Pieces

ABRSM Grade 7

Selected from the 2019 & 2020 syllabus

Name

Date o

Contents

page

LIST A

1 **George Frideric Handel** Gigue: fifth movement from Suite No. 8 in F minor, HWV 433 — 2

2 **Joseph Haydn** Tempo di Minuetto: third movement from Sonata in E flat, Hob. XVI:49 — 5

3 **Wolfgang Amadeus Mozart** Andante: second movement from Sonata in G, K. 283 — 10

LIST B

1 **Léo Delibes** Passepied: No. 6 from *Six airs de danse* — 14

2 **Felix Mendelssohn** Lied ohne Worte: No. 3 from *Lieder ohne Worte*, Op. 102 — 18

3 **Hubert Parry** Elizabeth: No. 2 from *Shulbrede Tunes* — 21

LIST C

1 **Richard Rodney Bennett** Rosemary's Waltz: No. 2 from *Tender is the Night* — 24

2 **Sergey Prokofiev** Ridicolosamente: No. 10 from *Visions fugitives*, Op. 22 — 26

3 **Cheryl Frances-Hoad** Commuterland — 28

Editor for ABRSM: Richard Jones

Other pieces for Grade 7

LIST A

4 **C. P. E. Bach** Allegro assai (1st movt from *Sonata in G*, H. 119, Wq. 62/19). *C. P. E. Bach: Piano Sonatas, Vol. 2* (Henle)

5 **J. S. Bach** Giga (7th movt from *Partita No. 1 in B♭*, BWV 825). *J. S. Bach: Partitas Nos. 1–3* (ABRSM) or *J. S. Bach: Six Partitas, BWV 825–830* (Bärenreiter)

6 **D. Scarlatti** Sonata in D minor, Kp. 1, L. 366 (Bärenreiter) or *D. Scarlatti: 200 Sonatas, Vol. 1* (Editio Musica Budapest)

LIST B

4 **Esplá** Canción de cuna (from *Suite de pequeñas piezas*). *Esplá: Música para piano* (UME)

5 **Gurlitt** Moderato grazioso: No. 7 from *Buds and Blossoms*, Op. 107 (Alfred)

6 **Skryabin** Prelude in B♭ minor: No. 4 from *Seven Preludes*, Op. 17 (Belaieff)

LIST C

4 **Peter Dickinson** Hymn-Tune Rag. *Peter Dickinson: Rags, Blues & Parodies* (Novello)

5 **Khachaturian** Allegro giocoso: 1st movt from *Sonatina* (Sikorski–Boosey & Hawkes or Peters)

6 **Christopher Norton** Mambo (No. 7 from *Latin Preludes 1*). *Christopher Norton: Latin Preludes Collection* (Boosey & Hawkes)

First published in 2018 by ABRSM (Publishing) Ltd,
a wholly owned subsidiary of ABRSM, 4 London Wall Place,
London EC2Y 5AU, United Kingdom
© 2018 by The Associated Board of the Royal Schools of Music
Distributed worldwide by Oxford University Press

Music origination by Julia Bovee
Cover by Kate Benjamin & Andy Potts, with thanks to Brighton College
Printed in England by Page Bros (Norwich) Ltd, on materials from
sustainable sources.
Reprinted in 2018

A:1

Gigue

Fifth movement from Suite No. 8 in F minor, HWV 433

G. F. Handel
(1685–1759)

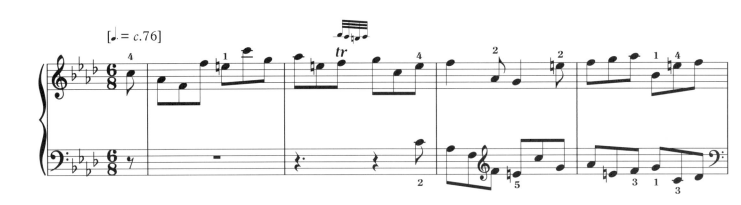

This Gigue is the finale of Handel's Suite in F minor, the last of the eight suites that he published in 1720. That publication contains a carefully planned selection and revision of his best and most mature keyboard works. In the F minor Suite, three stylized dances – Allemande, Courante and Gigue – are introduced by a substantial prelude and fugue.

This movement illustrates two characteristic features of the Baroque gigue: the treble theme is imitated by the bass at the lower octave (bb. 1–4 and 25–8); and the theme of the second half (bb. 25–8) is a free inversion of that of the first half.

Source: *Suites de pieces pour le clavecin, premier volume* (London, 1720)

Adapted from Handel: *Eight Great Suites*, Book II, edited by Richard Jones (ABRSM)

4

Tempo di Minuetto

Third movement from Sonata in E flat, Hob. XVI:49

Joseph Haydn
(1732–1809)

Haydn composed over 60 sonatas during a period of roughly 35 years (c.1761–95). The earlier sonatas were written for the harpsichord, but during 1783–95 he published ten sonatas for the fortepiano. These, alongside Mozart's sonatas of the 1780s, represent a high point of Viennese Classical style. This late group includes this Sonata in E flat, which was composed in about 1789/90 and first published in Vienna in 1791. The title of the finale, 'Tempo di Minuetto', indicates that the dance element, while clearly present, is modified or marginalized to some extent. In addition, the form is considerably expanded beyond the usual minuet and trio – this movement has two trios (at bb. 25 and 61), forming an overall rondo pattern, ABACA, in which C is a minor-mode variant of A.

Source: first edition, *Sonate pour le Clavecin ou Piano-Forte, Op. 66* (Vienna: Artaria [1791]). Slurs to grace notes have been added by the editor.

A:3

Andante

Second movement from Sonata in G, K. 283

W. A. Mozart
(1756–91)

The Sonata in G, K. 283, from which this Andante is selected, is the fifth of a set of six piano sonatas that the 19-year-old Mozart composed while staying in Munich in early 1775. They are his earliest surviving piano sonatas. In 1777 he wrote to his father Leopold from Augsburg: 'Here and at Munich I have played all my six sonatas [in public] by heart several times.'

Though early in date, this Andante is highly sophisticated in style and form. It is constructed in a miniature sonata form – exposition, 1st subject: b. 1; transition: b. 5; 2nd subject: b. 9; development: b. 15; and recapitulation: b. 24. Note-groups are often very carefully notated and articulated (e.g. bb. 5–6 and 9), revealing the composer's precise intentions. Note that the young Mozart used the wedge for standard staccato (bb. 5–6 etc.) and the dot for mezzo-staccato in groups of repeated notes (bb. 1 and 3 etc.).

Source: autograph, formerly in Staatsbibliothek zu Berlin; first edition, *Trois sonates, Op. 7* (Vienna: Christoph Torricella, 1784)

© 1979 by The Associated Board of the Royal Schools of Music
Adapted from Mozart: *Sonatas for Pianoforte*, Vol. I, edited by Stanley Sadie (ABRSM)

12

B:1

Passepied

No. 6 from *Six airs de danse*

Léo Delibes
(1836–91)

Delibes' *Six airs de danse dans le style ancien* (Six Dance Tunes in the Old Style) were written as incidental music for the 1882 revival of Victor Hugo's play *Le roi s'amuse* (The King has Fun). The play is about a hunchbacked court jester, and is set in Paris in the 1520s. In a clever, light-hearted manner, Delibes here freely imitates the French music of an earlier period.

The passepied, a lively Baroque dance in triple time, is treated here as a melodious dance in alla breve time with broken-chordal accompaniment. It is written in ternary form (ABA[1]), with the outer sections in C sharp minor and the central section in the submediant A major (b. 26). The A section is itself ternary, having a middle phrase in the relative major E (b. 10). When the A section returns (b. 34), it is modified from b. 50, particularly in harmony, to form a suitable ending.

Source: *Scène du bal: exécutée au Théâtre-français dans Le Roi s'amuse de Victor Hugo. Six Airs de Danse dans le style ancien* (Paris: Heugel, 1882)

© 2018 by The Associated Board of the Royal Schools of Music

Song without Words

Lied ohne Worte

No. 3 from *Lieder ohne Worte*, Op. 102

Felix Mendelssohn
(1809–47)

Felix Mendelssohn was a skilled player and improviser on piano and organ, and he wrote in all about 150 piano compositions. Among the most significant of these are the 48 *Lieder ohne Worte* (Songs without Words) – short pieces written in a lyrical, song-like style and texture. Of these, 36 were published between 1833 and 1845 in six volumes, each containing six pieces, and a further 12 pieces were published posthumously.

   This piece (composed in 1845), with its presto tempo, staccato touch and mostly *piano* dynamic, recalls Mendelssohn's personal style of scherzo, of which the most famous example is the first entr'acte from the incidental music to *A Midsummer Night's Dream*. Staccato is marked only in bb. 1, 2, 63 and 64, but it may be assumed elsewhere, too.

Sources: *Six Lieder ohne Worte, Op. 102* (London: Novello, Ewer [1867]); *Sechs Lieder ohne Worte, Op. 102* (Bonn: N. Simrock [1868])

Elizabeth

No. 2 from *Shulbrede Tunes*

B:3

Hubert Parry
(1848–1918)

Andantino grazioso [♩ = *c*.80]

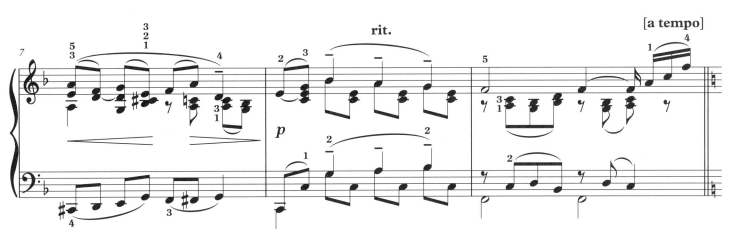

Hubert Parry taught at the Royal College of Music from when it opened in 1883, becoming director in 1894. He was also Professor of Music at Oxford University from 1900 to 1908. As a composer, he is widely regarded as one of the leading figures in late 19th-century English music.

The *Shulbrede Tunes*, begun in 1911, are named after Shulbrede Priory in the county of Sussex, which was by then a country house and had been bought by Parry's daughter in 1905. The 'tunes' form a Schumannesque series of musical portraits of the house and family. 'Elizabeth' refers to Parry's granddaughter, whom he described as 'a little slip of a girl, very springy in her gait.' The piece is written in ternary form (ABA plus coda), with a sharp contrast between the *grazioso* main section (bb. 1 and 24) and the *capriccioso* middle section (b. 10).

Source: *Shulbrede Tunes for Pianoforte* (London: Augener, 1914)

Rosemary's Waltz

No. 2 from *Tender is the Night*

Richard Rodney Bennett
(1936-2012)

Sir Richard Rodney Bennett studied at the Royal Academy of Music, London, with Lennox Berkeley and Howard Ferguson (1953–7), and then with Boulez in Paris (1957–9). Besides being a highly prolific and versatile composer, he was well known as a jazz pianist, and his strong interest in jazz often lent colour and vitality to his compositions.

'Rosemary's Waltz' is selected from *Tender is the Night*, which Bennett wrote in 1985 as the theme music for a BBC Television dramatization of the 1934 novel of that name by the American writer F. Scott Fitzgerald. Bennett's richly dissonant harmony breathes new life into the old genre of the Viennese waltz – the most popular of all 19th-century ballroom dances.

AB 3909

Ridiculously

Ridicolosamente

No. 10 from *Visions fugitives*, Op. 22

Sergey Prokofiev
(1891–1953)

Sergey Prokofiev composed music and played the piano from an early age. First taught by his mother, herself a pianist, he was writing his earliest piano pieces by the age of five. *Visions fugitives* (Fleeting Visions) dates from his early Russian period; it contains 20 pieces that originated in the period 1915–17 and was first published in 1922.

The piece selected here is aptly characterized by its expression mark, *ridicolosamente* (ridiculously). It well illustrates a recurring side of Prokofiev's musical personality – a sense of humour that constantly borders on the absurd, ludicrous and grotesque. At the time when it was written, the young composer was widely regarded as potentially dangerous, and he cultivated this image in avant-garde, anti-Romantic and (for its time) ultra-modern music, of which this piece is an excellent example.

Source: *Mimoletnosti – Visions fugitives. Nouvelle edition revue par l'auteur* (Moscow: A. Gutheil, *c.*1925)

© Copyright 1922 by Hawkes & Son (London) Ltd
Published in *Visions Fugitives*, Op. 22 (ISMN 979-0-060-081781)

Commuterland

Cheryl Frances-Hoad
(born 1980)

The English composer Cheryl Frances-Hoad studied at the Yehudi Menuhin School, Cambridge University, and King's College, London. She has written concertos, piano trios, an opera and *A Young Person's Guide to Composition*.

About this piece the composer has written: '*Commuterland* was written directly after I had had to do a long commute, every day for a week, for a project I was working on. The frustration of rush hour and being caught behind crowds walking slowly through [London] Underground tunnels is expressed in this piece! At the same time, I was listening to a lot of Bartók, and the repetitive motivic cells and harmonies are in part a homage to this composer, who is one of my idols.'